Space Art

Celia Warren

Illustrated by Andy Parker

RIGBY

Space Ant was lost.

"I want to go back home," she said.

"There's no place like home."

Then she came to a blue planet.

"I'll go and have a look," she said.

Space Ant got out.

"Brrr," she said.

"This blue planet is freezing cold!"

Along came a tigeroo.

"Hello," said Space Ant. "Isn't it cold here?"

"Yesss," said the tigeroo. "I don't like it here."

"Come with me to another planet,"
said Space Ant.

Off they went.

Next, they came to a red planet.

"Let's go and have a look," they said.

They got out.

"Phew!" said Space Ant.

"This red planet is boiling hot!"

Along came an elebird.

"Hello," said the tigeroo. "Isn't it hot here?"

"It's **too** hot," said the elebird. "I don't like it here."

"Come with us to another planet,"
said Space Ant.

Off they went.

They zoomed past lots of stars and
then they came to a purple planet.

"Let's go and have a look," they said.

They got out.

The purple planet was not too cold.

It was not too hot.

"This planet is just right," said the tigeroo.

"I love it!" said the elebird.

"I love it too," said Space Ant,
"because this is **my** planet."

"There's no place like home!"